The Five Places I Want To Visit After I Die.

A way to share your legacy with future generations of family and friends.

THE FIVE PLACES I WANT TO VISIT AFTER I DIE by John Graham. Published by FIGID Press
Brownsburg, IN 46112 www.FIGIDPress.com / FIGIDPress@Gmail.com
ISBN: 9781729043592

Dedication

This book is dedicated to my father. He felt connected to special locations from his life and asked that his ashes be spread in one of them. Since his passing, I don't feel an association with a simple plot of earth in a graveyard, but instead with a beautiful location filled with great memories of family moments. When I see that place, I think of him and the time we shared.

Thank you for purchasing this book! Take a look at the back pages for a special offer to make your legacy experience even better.

All the best! - John Graham

Table of Contents

About this book

This book isn't your typical personal workbook that will sit on a loved one's shelf to be looked through once or twice until ending up in a yardsale or Goodwill box. Instead, this book is your chance to tell future generations about you and the important places from your life.

The purpose of the book is for your children, close friends, and family members to use these pages as a guide to revisit significant places from your life. As they reach the different destinations, they will have an opportunity to reflect on your life and experiences, then leave a part of you in that special place.

This book will then become an interactive gateway between you and the generations to come, so prepare yourself to invest some time, effort, and inspiration for those that come after you. Think of this as more than just a journal that someone in the future will pick up and read once or twice. Instead, picture it as a memory book with a scavenger hunt component that allows people to gain a better understanding of you through the locations you have chosen.

Your goal with this journaling/legacy book will be to think of the five most significant places in your personal history and then write about them. Provide as much detail as you can, while reflecting on special memories to share. Beyond a simple description of the locations, you'll find additional pages in each section designed to help you list activities or reflections you would like others to experience in your absence. Use the following pages as a reference to gain more insight on what to expect.

Beyond a simple journal

The difference between this book and some other personal history activity books currently available is the goal for your loved ones to visit your special locations and leave a part of you there.

While the book is built around the idea of cremation and the spreading of your ashes at your chosen key locations around the world, it can still be used if you have fundamental issues with act of cremation.* If you choose not to be cremated, then simply identify five personal items or "tokens" to represent your spirit and have loved ones deliver those instead of your ashes. Your loved ones will still have that physical connection between you and the locations you have chosen.

While the act of delivering a part of you to the five special locations you identify is the focus of the book, you'll also find other sections that your family will greatly appreciate as a vehicle to remember you better. From places you've always wanted to visit to basic questions about who you are, this book has a lot to offer. There is also a section where you can update the book annually for years to come, making this a relevant book for now and the future.

*Disclaimer:
Please keep in mind that if you choose to incorporate the spreading of ashes with these activities, there are some places that aren't exactly o.k. with people coming along and placing human remains on their property. We would strongly recommend that your family do their research and also use their discretion when it comes to placing your remains in certain locations.

Sections of the Book

Your Five Locations

Take some time and reflect on the five most impactful locations from your life. It may take some pondering and narrowing down, but you can do it.

Dream Locations

Everyone has those one or two places they've always thought about visiting, but never had the chance. Make a note of them here so future generations can mentally bring you along when they go.

Extra Things About Me

Your favorite food, color, memory, and more are here for you to write about. Use the prompts on the pages to help others get a better understanding of who you are and what makes you tick.

My Life Story

Plenty of pages for you to write about your life, your experiences, and the things that shaped you into the person you are today. Share your story with generations to come.

Year in Review

Just because you filled out the book doesn't mean you will stop living your life. This section has places to record significant events for years to come, so keep everyone updated on what's going on.

Choosing your top five.

The following pages will get you thinking about how to approach the location questions you will fill out.

Location Choices – The parts of the page

Overview:

Each location that you come up with should have a deep significance to you and potentially those in your family for years to come. Beyond the name and address, there are additional sections to help you get your emotional connection across.

Even if your location no longer exists, you can still use the provided picture pages to tape an envelope with pictures of how it used to be. You can also record weblinks or other reference material to help them access pictures to visualize the location better when they arrive at your destination.

Name:

This area can contain the official name of the location, such as Gettysburg, or a more personal reflection like "My First House".

Address:

While many locations will have a specific address for you to reference, you will encounter some situations where GPS coordinates may be more practical. These can be obtained with a cell phone app in most cases and will help loved ones pinpoint more specific places. That special spot by a lake where you had your first kiss doesn't necessarily have a street sign.

Other References:

To help better capture the spirit of your location from over the years, do your research and find links on the internet about your location or even books that can be read about it.

Other locations nearby:

This is a great place to list other areas or activities people can visit when they make the trip to the locations you have chosen.

Why did you pick the location:

What makes this place special to you and potentially others? This is a great opportunity to give an overview of this location and some of its key attributes.

My specific memories section:

There are extra pages here for you to write out some key memories that center around the picked location. List as many details as you can think of to help others visualize your experiences there. Don't just record your recent memories of the location, but instead try and pick your favorite moments from over the years. The memories don't have to be just about you and your experiences, instead try and incorporate special times with your family and friends.

What do you enjoy doing:

Maybe your special location is a lake that you enjoyed canoeing on or had that family picnic spot. Maybe it was the local restaurant you stopped for ice cream after you left that lake with your family. Think of something you may have loved doing at the locations you select and recommend they give it a try in your memory. Help others to feel the joy or excitement from your history.

What activity should others do when they visit:

You likely know the location better than anyone else, so put your recommendations here for the future generations.

Other activities in the area:

Here's where you talk about things to do in the area. You might have a location in Gettysburg as your main choice, but this section is the place where you might list a side trip to nearby Harrisburg or Carlisle to enjoy some other Civil War museums you loved.

Picture Pages

Use this spread to tape pictures of your location or of you at the location. If you don't think a menagerie of pictures is your style, then tape envelopes there. Fill them with any pictures that will help you show the emotion you feel about this special place in your life.

Post Mortem Pages

The post mortem pages might be challenging for you to fill out, because if you're like most people, it's tough to think about what will happen after you die. Don't feel too much apprehension as you sit down to write out instructions to others for after you pass, they will appreciate you investing the time and energy more than you will ever know.

Who you'd like as part of the group:
Different locations from your past will have special significance to different people in your life. You may ask that some locations involve just your family members, while others you might want to include special friends who are linked to that location with you.

Specific location and method to spread ashes or place token:
This portion is where you share your final wishes for a part of you to be joined with your selected location.

Activity or reflection you'd like performed during the spreading of ashes or placing of token:
Maybe you want someone specific to say a few words during the moment, or possibly a poem read, or memory shared.

Actions or Activities to be performed after the spreading or placement:
What better way to have folks celebrate your life than through an activity at your special location that you think will strengthen their connection to it.

Location Example

The following pages are an example how you can fill out the workbook.

Name:

Our family home, and more specifically the large oak tree in the back corner of the yard.

Address or GPS Coordinates:

1234 Any Street Blvd

Any Town, USA 12345

Latitude 40.321 Longitude -80.68

Weblinks and other references about location:

www.TownName.org

www.HomesofInterest.com/our house (the house was featured in an article during Christmas 2001)

www.Facebook.com/mypage/pictures/thehouse

Other locations nearby: (Check these out too!)

Our family church is at:

Schools are: (I spent a lot of time at them watching events for my kids, so I almost felt like an attending student).

Williamson Park - a special park near our house that I enjoyed visiting, especially in the Fall when the leaves changed.

So much of my life revolved around our house and the thirty years we spent living there. We bought it almost new and I helped to plant the trees in the backyard as saplings.

Over the years I watched the trees and our family grow, becoming more connected with each passing season. We stayed here because of the house, the trees, the town, and the amazing atmosphere to raise a family. We had opportunities to move, but it was important to me that we have a "home base" for our family.

The kids went off to build their own lives, but we all made it a point to gather up whenever we could to celebrate our continuing lives. This mindset and the imporantance of this place made this location an obvious choice.

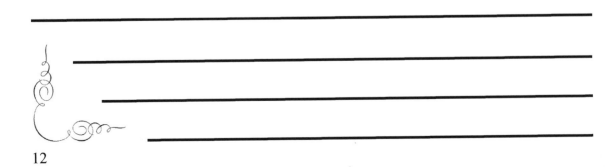

Why Did I Pick This Location?

What makes this place special to me and potentially others.

I have so many wonderful memories of this house that it will be tough to list just a few. These are the most significant to me and I wanted to share them.

I remember planting the oak tree the week after my first child (Mary) was born as a celebration of becoming a father. I had never planted a tree before and I dug the hole much too deep. The day was hot and my wife (Alice) gave me such a hard time when she saw the huge hole next to a small tree. It took me a while to fill it back in, but that moment stuck with me. Over the next few years, I planted three more trees along that line, making it a tradition for each of my kids.

Every Christmas I made it a point the deck out the house for the holidays. The frame of our roof was perfect for light strands and the occaisional blow mold. It was tough work, but I always felt a sense of satisfaction after it was done. I loved getting compliments from folks as they traveled through the neighborhood. I put a picture of my favorite year in the picture page section.

I always considered myself pretty handy around the house and tried to do most repairs myself. I had a few mishaps in the beginning, but if you look around, you'll see that most updates were done by my hand. Over the years and many projects, I found it fun to leave little notes about me or the family in my repairs for future generations to find. Here's a few to look for as renovations are done in the future.

1. Behind the bathroom mirror in the master bath.

2. In the attic by the stairway under the plyboard.

3. The underside of kitchen drawers.

As the big oak tree grew through the years, it became such an important part of my life. Providing shade in the Summer, leaf piles in the Fall, and something to climb year round. In my time on this Earth, I experienced every emotion you imagine in the shade of that tree. It stayed strong with us as our kids grew and moved on with their own lives.

This is what makes it one of my five locations.

What do I enjoy doing at the location?

Beyond the classic backyard activities, I have a couple of special things with the tree that I enjoyed over the years.

On the Southwest side of the tree, under the biggest branch if it's still there, was the perfect spot on the ground to stretch out and feel completely connected with nature. There were some days in the Summer and Fall where I would just get a blanket and lay there. Sometimes I would read a book and other times I would just watch the sky as clouds rolled by.

The backyard also has the perfect amount of space for a great soccer game, using the two big trees on one end and the porch posts on the other. I want to say that this was the official family activity because everyone would be involved and have a good time.

The house had the perfect amount of space for us and our growing family through the years and I enjoyed every moment.

What activity should others do when they visit?

I definitely feel that the family soccer challenge must be continued, so bring a ball and lace up your shoes for an epic all-ages game.

I'd also like to encourage each of my kids to take a walk around the neighborhood with their families and point out some significant spots from their childhoods. So many important things happened on these streets and the grandkids need to know how this place helped shape our family into what it is today.

Other activities in the area I recommend.

Our town has so many great things to do and see, so plan some extra time for exploration. The Children's Museum on main street would be great for the families and the big park on Adams avenue has the amazing trail through the woods. Grab a bite to eat at "The Jumbo Burger" place which was considered our family's special eatery.

Who I'd like to be part of the group visiting.

As much as the family that can make it would be great to have there. It's important to me that the grandkids realize the importance of these special trees and this place.

I'd also like it if any of the Jones family members could make it too. Their family was always welcome at our events and such an important part of our lives.

Location or method to spread my ashes (or place token).

I'd love to have a portion of my ashes buried just below the surface on the Southwest side of that first large tree, in the spot I loved to lay in and watch the clouds float by.

Having myself become part of that great place and eternally connected will make me happy, especially as future generations find themselves visiting it.

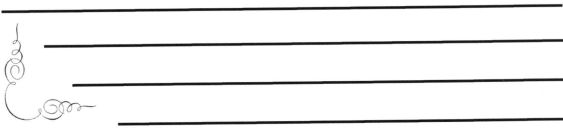

Activity or reflection to do during the spreading.

I'd love to have those there just share a moment that they experienced in the backyard or around the trees. Feel free to share one that involved me or not, just whatever is special to them.

_____

_____

_____

_____

_____

_____

_____

_____

_____

Actions or activities after spreading ashes.

Have a barbeque, play some backyard games, enjoy some good drinks and food. Make new memories in this wonderful place that will stick with you for years to come.

_____

_____

_____

Location Number One

Use the following pages to record your
experiences, thoughts, and things you did.

Name:

_____

Address or GPS Coordinates:

_____

_____

Weblinks and other references about location:

_____

_____

_____

_____

Other locations nearby: (Check these out too!)

_____

_____

_____

_____

_____

What makes this place special to me and potentially others.

My Memories Of This Place

These specific things have tied this location closely to my life.

My Memories Of This Place

These specific things have tied this location closely to my life.

My Memories Of This Place

These specific things have tied this location closely to my life.

What do I enjoy doing at the location?

Activities

What activity should others do when they visit?

_____

_____

_____

_____

_____

_____

_____

_____

_____

_____

_____

Other activities in the area I recommend.

_____

_____

_____

_____

_____

_____

Who I'd like to be part of the group visiting.

_____

_____

_____

_____

_____

_____

_____

Location or method to spread my ashes (or place token).

_____

_____

_____

_____

_____

_____

_____

_____

_____

_____

Post Mortem Requests

Activity or reflection to take place during the placement of ashes or token.

_____

_____

_____

_____

_____

_____

_____

_____

_____

_____

Actions or activities for after placement of ashes or token.

_____

_____

_____

_____

_____

_____

Loved One's Reflection Journal

Notes from family and friends who experienced the location after my passing.

Loved One's Reflection Journal

Notes from family and friends who experienced the location after my passing.

Loved One's Reflection Journal

Notes from family and friends who experienced the location after my passing.

Location Number Two

Use the following pages to record your
experiences, thoughts, and things you did.

Name:

_____

_____

Address or GPS Coordinates:

_____

_____

_____

Weblinks and other references about location:

_____

_____

_____

_____

_____

Other locations nearby: (Check these out too!)

_____

_____

_____

_____

_____

_____

Why Did I Pick This Location?

What makes this place special to me and potentially others.

My Memories Of This Place

These specific things have tied this location closely to my life.

44

My Memories Of This Place

These specific things have tied this location closely to my life.

What do I enjoy doing at the location?

_____

_____

_____

_____

_____

_____

_____

_____

_____

_____

_____

_____

_____

_____

_____

_____

_____

Activities

What activity should others do when they visit?

_____

_____

_____

_____

_____

_____

_____

_____

_____

_____

Other activities in the area I recommend.

_____

_____

_____

_____

_____

_____

Who I'd like to be part of the group visiting.

_____

_____

_____

_____

_____

_____

Location or method to spread my ashes (or place token).

_____

_____

_____

_____

_____

_____

_____

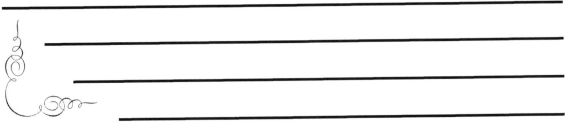

Post Mortem Requests

Activity or reflection to take place during the placement of ashes or token.

_____

_____

_____

_____

_____

_____

_____

_____

_____

_____

_____

Actions or activities for after placement of ashes or token.

_____

_____

_____

_____

_____

_____

Loved One's Reflection Journal

Notes from family and friends who experienced the location after my passing.

Loved One's Reflection Journal

Notes from family and friends who experienced the location after my passing.

Loved One's Reflection Journal

Notes from family and friends who experienced the location after my passing.

Location Number Three

Use the following pages to record your
experiences, thoughts, and things you did.

Name:

_____

Address or GPS Coordinates:

_____

_____

Weblinks and other references about location:

_____

_____

_____

_____

_____

Other locations nearby: (Check these out too!)

_____

_____

_____

_____

_____

What makes this place special to me and potentially others.

My Memories Of This Place

These specific things have tied this location closely to my life.

My Memories Of This Place

These specific things have tied this location closely to my life.

My Memories Of This Place

These specific things have tied this location closely to my life.

_____

_____

_____

_____

_____

_____

_____

_____

_____

_____

_____

_____

_____

_____

_____

_____

_____

_____

What do I enjoy doing at the location?

Activities

What activity should others do when they visit?

_____

_____

_____

_____

_____

_____

_____

_____

_____

_____

_____

Other activities in the area I recommend.

_____

_____

_____

_____

_____

Who I'd like to be part of the group visiting.

_____

_____

_____

_____

_____

_____

Location or method to spread my ashes (or place token).

_____

_____

_____

_____

_____

_____

_____

_____

Post Mortem Requests

Activity or reflection to take place during the placement of ashes or token.

_____

_____

_____

_____

_____

_____

_____

_____

_____

_____

_____

Actions or activities for after placement of ashes or token.

_____

_____

_____

_____

_____

Loved One's Reflection Journal

Notes from family and friends who experienced the location after my passing.

Loved One's Reflection Journal

Notes from family and friends who experienced the location after my passing.

Loved One's Reflection Journal

Notes from family and friends who experienced the location after my passing.

Location Number Four

Use the following pages to record your experiences, thoughts, and things you did.

Name:

_____

Address or GPS Coordinates:

_____

_____

Weblinks and other references about location:

_____

_____

_____

_____

Other locations nearby: (Check these out too!)

_____

_____

_____

_____

_____

_____

Why Did I Pick This Location?

What makes this place special to me and potentially others.

My Memories Of This Place

These specific things have tied this location closely to my life.

My Memories Of This Place

These specific things have tied this location closely to my life.

My Memories Of This Place

These specific things have tied this location closely to my life.

_____

_____

_____

_____

_____

_____

_____

_____

_____

_____

_____

_____

_____

_____

_____

_____

_____

_____

_____

_____

_____

What do I enjoy doing at the location?

_____

_____

_____

_____

_____

_____

_____

_____

_____

_____

_____

_____

_____

_____

_____

_____

_____

_____

Activities

What activity should others do when they visit?

_____

_____

_____

_____

_____

_____

_____

_____

_____

_____

Other activities in the area I recommend.

_____

_____

_____

_____

_____

Who I'd like to be part of the group visiting.

_____

_____

_____

_____

_____

_____

Location or method to spread my ashes (or place token).

_____

_____

_____

_____

_____

_____

_____

_____

Post Mortem Requests

Activity or reflection to take place during the placement of ashes or token.

_____

_____

_____

_____

_____

_____

_____

_____

_____

_____

_____

_____

Actions or activities for after placement of ashes or token.

_____

_____

_____

_____

_____

_____

Loved One's Reflection Journal

Notes from family and friends who experienced the location after my passing.

Loved One's Reflection Journal

Notes from family and friends who experienced the location after my passing.

Loved One's Reflection Journal

Notes from family and friends who experienced the location after my passing.

Location Number Five

Use the following pages to record your experiences, thoughts, and things you did.

Name:

_____

Address or GPS Coordinates:

_____

_____

Weblinks and other references about location:

_____

_____

_____

_____

Other locations nearby: (Check these out too!)

_____

_____

_____

_____

_____

_____

Why Did I Pick This Location?

What makes this place special to me and potentially others.

My Memories Of This Place

These specific things have tied this location closely to my life.

My Memories Of This Place

These specific things have tied this location closely to my life.

My Memories Of This Place

These specific things have tied this location closely to my life.

What do I enjoy doing at the location?

_____

_____

_____

_____

_____

_____

_____

_____

_____

_____

_____

_____

_____

_____

_____

_____

Activities

What activity should others do when they visit?

_____

_____

_____

_____

_____

_____

_____

_____

_____

_____

_____

Other activities in the area I recommend.

_____

_____

_____

_____

_____

Who I'd like to be part of the group visiting.

_____

_____

_____

_____

_____

_____

Location or method to spread my ashes (or place token).

_____

_____

_____

_____

_____

_____

_____

_____

Post Mortem Requests

Activity or reflection to take place during the placement of ashes or token.

_____

_____

_____

_____

_____

_____

_____

_____

_____

_____

_____

Actions or activities for after placement of ashes or token.

_____

_____

_____

_____

_____

_____

Loved One's Reflection Journal

Notes from family and friends who experienced the location after my passing.

Loved One's Reflection Journal

Notes from family and friends who experienced the location after my passing.

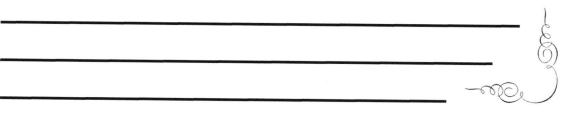

Loved One's Reflection Journal

Notes from family and friends who experienced the location after my passing.

Dream Locations I always wanted to visit.

I never got there, but if you make it, then please keep me in mind when you see the sights.

Name:

_____

_____

Address or GPS Coordinates:

_____

_____

_____

Weblinks and other references about the location:

_____

_____

_____

_____

_____

_____

Other nearby areas that would interest me.

_____

_____

_____

_____

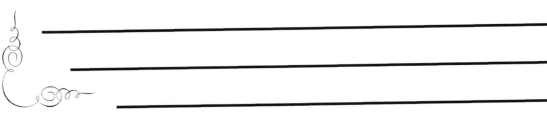

_____

_____

What makes this my dream destination?

_____

_____

_____

_____

_____

_____

_____

_____

_____

_____

_____

_____

_____

_____

_____

_____

_____

_____

What activities would I want to do there?

_____

_____

_____

_____

_____

_____

_____

_____

_____

_____

_____

What else would I do when in the area?

_____

_____

_____

_____

_____

_____

Loved One's Reflection Journal of Dream Location Visit

You had a chance to visit the location. What did you think?

Dream Location #2

Name:

_____

_____

Address or GPS Coordinates:

_____

_____

Weblinks and other references about the location:

_____

_____

_____

_____

Other nearby areas that would interest me.

_____

_____

_____

_____

_____

_____

What makes this my dream destination?

_____

_____

_____

_____

_____

_____

_____

_____

_____

_____

_____

_____

_____

_____

_____

_____

_____

_____

What activities would I want to do there?

_____

_____

_____

_____

_____

_____

_____

_____

_____

_____

What else would I do when in the area?

_____

_____

_____

_____

_____

_____

Loved One's Reflection Journal of Dream Location Visit

You had a chance to visit the location. What did you think?

Extra Things you might want to know about who I am

The following pages contain quick insights into who I am and what I'm thinking right now.

My favorite quote is:

_____

_____

_____

My favorite drink is:

_____

_____

_____

My favorite foods:

_____

_____

_____

My all time favorite songs are:

_____

_____

_____

_____

My favorite books of all time are:

_____

_____

_____

_____

My favorite sports teams are:

_____

_____

_____

_____

These are my all-time favorite TV shows:

_____

_____

_____

_____

These are my favorite movies:

_____

_____

_____

_____

My favorite color and if it ever changed:

_____

_____

_____

_____

My favorite game:

_____

_____

_____

_____

My hobbies are:

_____

_____

_____

_____

My dream job would be:

_____

_____

_____

_____

My favorite pet was:

_____

_____

_____

_____

The most interesting place I've been is:

_____

_____

_____

_____

My favorite birthday was:

_____

_____

_____

_____

The type of art that moves me is:

_____

_____

_____

_____

My favorite car was:

_____

_____

_____

My best friend is:

_____

_____

_____

My favorite smell is:

_____

_____

_____

My favorite subject in school was:

_____

_____

_____

My most memorable gift received was:

_____

_____

_____

I am most afraid of:

_____

_____

_____

My luckiest moment was:

_____

_____

_____

My strangest moment was:

_____

_____

_____

A song that best describes me is:

_____

_____

_____

_____

A movie character that is most like me is:

_____

_____

_____

_____

My most liked President of the U. S. was:

_____

_____

_____

_____

My least liked President of the U. S. was:

_____

_____

_____

_____

My religion is:

_____

_____

_____

My favorite charity is:

_____

_____

_____

When I'm bored, I like to:

_____

_____

_____

My favorite recreational activity is:

_____

_____

_____

My Life Story - A brief history of me

Much like a chest filled with treasure, the following pages contain a history of my life. Travel through these pages to experience my history and key moments that helped make me who I am.

The year in review Section

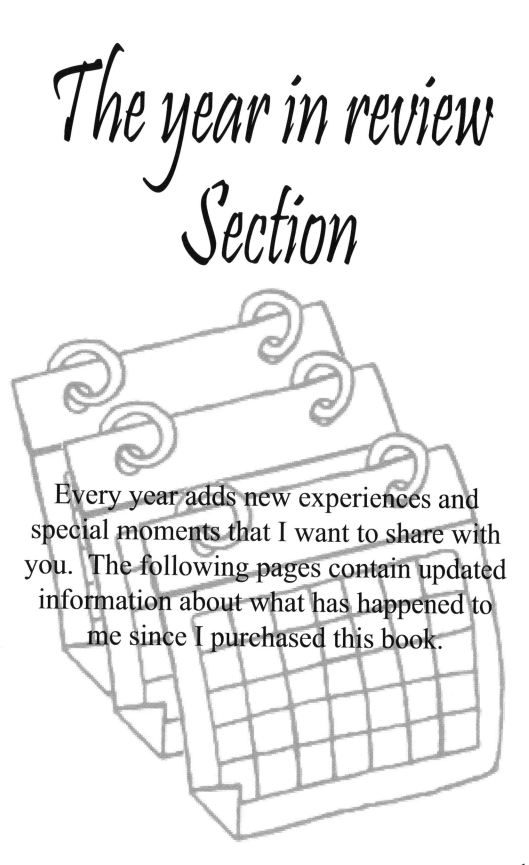

Every year adds new experiences and special moments that I want to share with you. The following pages contain updated information about what has happened to me since I purchased this book.

My year in review for

Significant Events:

_____

_____

_____

_____

_____

_____

_____

Family Moments:

_____

_____

_____

_____

_____

_____

_____

_____

Goals Accomplished:

_____

_____

_____

New Things Learned:

_____

_____

_____

Significant Purchases:

_____

_____

_____

Extra Information:

_____

_____

_____

_____

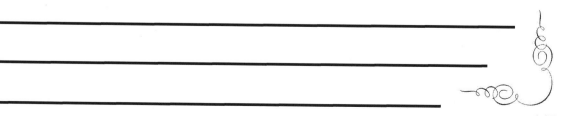

My year in review for

Significant Events:

_____

_____

_____

_____

_____

_____

_____

Family Moments:

_____

_____

_____

_____

_____

_____

_____

Goals Accomplished:

_____

_____

_____

New Things Learned:

_____

_____

_____

Significant Purchases:

_____

_____

_____

Extra Information:

_____

_____

_____

_____

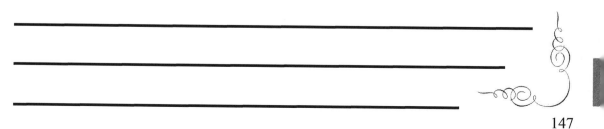

My year in review for

Significant Events:

_____

_____

_____

_____

_____

_____

Family Moments:

_____

_____

_____

_____

_____

_____

_____

Goals Accomplished:

_____

_____

_____

New Things Learned:

_____

_____

_____

Significant Purchases:

_____

_____

_____

Extra Information:

_____

_____

_____

_____

My year in review for

Significant Events:

_____

_____

_____

_____

_____

_____

_____

Family Moments:

_____

_____

_____

_____

_____

_____

_____

_____

Goals Accomplished:

_____

_____

_____

New Things Learned:

_____

_____

_____

Significant Purchases:

_____

_____

_____

Extra Information:

_____

_____

_____

_____

My year in review for

Significant Events:

_____

_____

_____

_____

_____

_____

Family Moments:

_____

_____

_____

_____

_____

_____

_____

Goals Accomplished:

_____

_____

_____

New Things Learned:

_____

_____

_____

Significant Purchases:

_____

_____

_____

Extra Information:

_____

_____

_____

_____

My year in review for

Significant Events:

_____

_____

_____

_____

_____

_____

_____

_____

Family Moments:

_____

_____

_____

_____

_____

_____

_____

_____

_____

Goals Accomplished:

_____

_____

_____

New Things Learned:

_____

_____

_____

Significant Purchases:

_____

_____

_____

Extra Information:

_____

_____

_____

_____

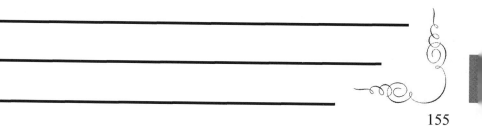

My year in review for

Significant Events:

_____

_____

_____

_____

_____

_____

_____

Family Moments:

_____

_____

_____

_____

_____

_____

_____

Goals Accomplished:

_____

_____

_____

New Things Learned:

_____

_____

_____

Significant Purchases:

_____

_____

_____

Extra Information:

_____

_____

_____

_____

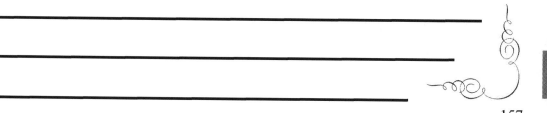

My year in review for

Significant Events:

_____

_____

_____

_____

_____

_____

_____

Family Moments:

_____

_____

_____

_____

_____

_____

_____

Goals Accomplished:

_____

_____

_____

New Things Learned:

_____

_____

_____

Significant Purchases:

_____

_____

_____

Extra Information:

_____

_____

_____

_____

My year in review for

Significant Events:

_____

_____

_____

_____

_____

_____

_____

Family Moments:

_____

_____

_____

_____

_____

_____

_____

_____

Goals Accomplished:

_____

_____

_____

New Things Learned:

_____

_____

_____

Significant Purchases:

_____

_____

_____

Extra Information:

_____

_____

_____

_____

My year in review for

Significant Events:

_____

_____

_____

_____

_____

_____

_____

Family Moments:

_____

_____

_____

_____

_____

_____

_____

Goals Accomplished:

_____

_____

_____

New Things Learned:

_____

_____

_____

Significant Purchases:

_____

_____

_____

Extra Information:

_____

_____

_____

_____

Name	Relationship	Date of Birth

Name	Relationship	Date of Birth

Name	Relationship	Date of Birth

Family Names, Dates, and Relationships

Name	Relationship	Date of Birth

Want to make this book even more special? We have a unique offer just for you!

Here at FIGID Press, we know how important it is to create lasting memories and then sharing them with future generations. From our first published book, "No Sweets For Santa", our goal was to create new family traditions that would last over the years. The book you are holding in your hands continues the desire to see people share parts of themselves that their children and their children's children can hold onto forever.

While this book stands up well if you take the time to fill it out, we realize that it's just one copy and things may happen to it over the years. We know that you likely don't want to buy ten copies and rewrite everything ten times over so your family and friends each have a copy, so we have a solution.

After you complete the main parts of the book, such as the locations, dream locations, extra things about you, and your story; you can contact us to transfer everything into a printed edition. This will give you the flexibility to order as many copies as you'd like for friends and family, so they each have their own copy. Our goal is to make the price and process economical and efficient, so it would be similar to purchasing average Christmas gifts for everyone on your list. Timeframes and pricing will be based on the number of copies you need and the amount of special formatting required. Of course, your book will also have a personalized cover, making it even more special for your family and friends.

Finally I Got it Done!

What makes this a great option for you is that your family and loved ones will be able to utilize their own copies to record their thoughts and reflections from their perspectives, which in turn would be kept for their family's future. Over time, they may even begin a library containing books from all family members to create a unique perspective of their loved one's lives.

Beyond the printed copies of the book, your original copy would also be returned to you, along with any specific pictures or information you provided to be included. We want you to have as much information to share with those you love.

How to order:

Contact: John Graham
At
FIGIDPRESS@Gmail.com

Get more information and talk through the variety of options for your personalized copies for family and friends.

Notes of things I need to collect for the book:

Made in the USA
Lexington, KY
16 November 2018